Heart Smart

COOKING ON A
SHOESTRING

JULIE WATSON

HEART
AND STROKE
FOUNDATION
OF CANADA

Macmillan Canada
Toronto, Ontario, Canada

Canadian Cataloguing in Publication Data

Watson, Julie V., date.
Heart Smart cooking on a shoestring
Includes index

ISBN 0-7715-9121-7

1. Low-cholesterol diet - Recipes.   2. Heart - Diseases - Prevention.   I. Title.

RC684.D5W3 1991   641.5'6311   C91-094521-7

1 2 3 4 5 WC 95 94 93 92 91

Cover design by Don Fernley
Cover photo by Fred Bird
Cover photo: Hearty Vegetable Soup (page 14)
Illustrations by Emma Hesse

Macmillan Canada
A Division of Canada Publishing Corporation
Toronto, Ontario, Canada

Printed in Canada

CONTENTS

ACKNOWLEDGEMENTS

The author would like to thank the following for their assistance in the research, recipe development and creation of this book:

Prince Edward Island Cookbook Committee Members:
Karen Jones, Education Director, Heart and Stroke Foundation of P.E.I. who worked closely with me during the early phases of the project
Elizabeth Newson, Committee Chair, Nutrition Coordinator, P.E.I. Department of Health and Social Services
Debbie McCrady, Marketing Home Economist, P.E.I. Hog and Egg Marketing Boards
Valerie Kelly, Home Economist, Extension Marketing Representative, P.E.I. Department of Agriculture
Shelley Murphy, Home Economist, P.E.I. Department of Fisheries and Aquaculture
Donalda Clow, Education Director, Heart and Stroke Foundation of P.E.I.

Also:
Carol Dombrow, Nutrition Consultant, Heart and Stroke Foundation of Canada
Ethel Beamish, Metro Social Services, Toronto, Ontario
Ellen DesJardin, Community Nutritionist, City of Toronto, Department of Public Health, Toronto, Ontario
Pam Hatton, Heart Smart Coordinator, Heart and Stroke Foundation of Nova Scotia, Halifax, Nova Scotia
Karen J. Johnston, Director of Education, Heart and Stroke Foundation of Manitoba, Winnipeg, Manitoba
Carolyn Chu, Nutritionist, Child Hunger and Education Program, Saskatoon Community Health Unit, Saskatoon, Saskatchewan
Suzanne Mahaffey, Nutritionist, Heart Health Project, Saskatoon Community Health Unit, Saskatoon, Saskatchewan
Margo E. Bent, Nutrition Consultant, Fredericton, New Brunswick
Patti Slattery, BCDNA Representative, Vancouver General Hospital, Vancouver, British Columbia
British Columbia Dieticians and Nutritionists Association, Vancouver, British Columbia
Hugeuette Cloutir, RDN, Reach Community Centre, Vancouver, British Columbia
Joanne Leslie, Director of Education and Communications, B.C. and Yukon Heart Foundation, Vancouver, British Columbia
Jean K. Thompson, Community Nutritionist, North Shore Health, Vancouver, British Columbia
Elderly Services Branch, Metro Social Services, Toronto, Ontario

I would also like to thank the numerous senior citizens, organizations, food writers, grocery store staff, food bank staff, and others who gave me insight into what Canadians eat, why and what they can do to improve eating habits when their budget is restricted.

Julie V. Watson

INTRODUCTION

This book has been created to introduce Heart Smart choices to home cooking. Casseroles, soups, stews, pizzas, sandwiches and snacks have been slimmed down to show you how to give your old favourites a healthier look. Based on *Canada's Guidelines for Healthy Eating*, these recipes will show you how Heart Smart eating can fit into your lifestyle. Heart Smart cooking doesn't have to be expensive—cabbage, potatoes, turnip and other vegetables that were staples of earlier generations have been used to provide good nutrition and keep costs down. Rediscover them in low-fat dishes that are easy on your food budget.

The secret to staying within your budget is to plan your meals (and snacks) before you go to the grocery store and shop only for those items that you need. With the right ingredients on hand, these easy-to-prepare recipes will put some variety into your weekly food routines and be enjoyable to prepare. Simply plan according to the four food groups when you make your shopping list.

There is no question that the first venture into Heart Smart cooking is a challenge, but no big changes are really necessary. Meals prepared with less fat can taste every bit as good as their overweight cousins—soon you will find that your tastes have changed and you're on your way to a Heart Smart lifestyle.

Canada's Guidelines for Healthy Eating (1991)

Enjoy a variety of foods.

Emphasize cereals, breads, other grain products, vegetables and fruits.

Choose lower-fat dairy products, leaner meats and foods prepared with little or no fat.

Achieve and maintain a healthy body weight by enjoying regular physical activity and healthy eating.

Limit salt, alcohol and caffeine.

The food your body needs every day can be divided into four groups:

Grains
Vegetables and Fruits
Milk Products
Meat and Alternates

Grains

Whole grain breads, pasta and cereals will give you both fibre and the energy your body needs. They are good for you and should be a main part of your diet.

This group includes breads, cereals, pasta, rice, bulgur, and couscous. Try to choose whole grain varieties whenever possible.

Vegetables and Fruits

This group has lots of fibre and vitamins, and little, if any fat. Fruits and vegetables are also low in calories. If you're going to overload on any food group—this is the one to choose. Cooking fruits and vegetables will reduce the fibre content so eat them raw if you want to get the most fibre.

Choose dark yellow and dark green vegetables such as spinach, broccoli, squash or carrots often, and you will get greater amounts of vitamins. Usually the darker the colour, the more vitamins the vegetable will have.

Storing and cooking vegetables and fruits properly is key to preserving as much of the nutrition as possible. Most should be kept in a cool, dry place and should be used soon after you purchase them.

Milk Products

Milk is a major source of calcium, which is needed to maintain healthy bones and teeth. Without milk products it is very difficult to obtain the calcium you need. Look for skim, partly-skimmed or lower-fat choices to lower the fat content of all dairy products. Children under the age of 2 are the exception to this suggestion; they should be on whole milk if not on breast milk or formula.

This group includes milk, yogurt and all kinds of cheese. The important thing is to select the lower-fat varieties.

On a per cup (250 mL) comparison, here's how the different milks stack up:

	Calories	Grams of Fat
Whole or homogenized milk	158	9
2% milk	124	5
1% milk	108	2.7
Buttermilk	105	2
Skim milk	90	trace

Most families resist drinking skim milk. Try to switch to 2% or even 1% for drinking and use skim milk or non-fat instant dry milk powder for cooking.

If you need to save money on milk, mix equal parts of 2% milk with skim milk made from powder. Refrigerate overnight, then strain it to eliminate any undissolved particles. No matter what your budget, don't stop using milk—it is too good for you to give up. Just use the lower-fat types where you can.

For the most savings, remember that fluid milk costs more than twice as much as milk made from skim milk powder. Substituting milk from skim milk powder for fluid milk could save a family of four (who are regular milk drinkers) about ten dollars a week or over five hundred dollars a year!

The best choices for yogurt are those with 2% or less fat. The best buys are large containers of plain yogurt that can be used in cooking or dressed up with fruit, vanilla flavouring, honey or granola.

Cheese is also an excellent source of calcium and protein, however, it can be high in fat.

• If you have a meal containing high fat foods, such as macaroni and cheese or fried fish, then cut back other high-fat foods in your meal, such as spreads on bread, fatty desserts and salad dressings. Balance the meal with a salad, vegetables, whole grain bread or fresh fruit.

• Lower-fat or skim milk cheese will not have as strong a flavour as you may be used to. Experiment until you find the ones you like. Try combining a strong-flavoured cheese such as Parmesan with a lower-fat cheese to give you more flavour with fewer fats.

• For sandwiches or cracker snacks, zip up lower-fat cheese by adding a little mustard, salsa, chili sauce, Worcestershire sauce or a sprinkle of cayenne or curry powder.

Meat and Alternates

Choose lean meat, fish or poultry as meal choices. Red meats are a good source of iron. Protein-rich foods such as dried peas, beans and lentils are high in fibre and make a healthy change from meat. Peanut butter, nuts and seeds are considered alternates but because they are higher in fat, choose them less often.

Eggs are also part of this group. Unless you have a high cholesterol level, eggs in moderation are an economical choice for a varied, healthy diet. Variety is the key.

Fat Fighters

- For every teaspoon (5 mL) of butter, margarine or oil you cut out, you save 4 grams of fat. That might be as much as 8 grams of fat a day if you don't butter your toast, sandwich, muffin or popover! (And it will save you money.)

- If you enjoy a cup of coffee or tea, use milk or skim milk powder rather than powdered coffee creamers.

- Snack foods such as chips, pop, cakes and pastries are often high in fat, sugar and salt and so low in nutrients that snack foods are not included in the food groups. Check the section on snacks to find some lower-fat alternatives.

- Choose a broth-based soup or make the recipes for creamed soups in this book.

- Drink lower-fat milk or fruit juices with your meals.

- Choose:
  - skim milk instead of 1%
  - 2% instead of whole milk
  - cottage cheese and yogurt with 2% or less milkfat
  - cheese with lower milkfat content
  - sherbet or frozen yogurt instead of ice cream

- If you think your dinner will leave you hungry, fill up on extra rice or a slice of whole grain bread instead of cookies, cake or higher-fat baked goods.

- Go easy on fast foods and convenience or pre-mixed foods.

Shopping Tips

- Plan meals ahead of time and make a list of the food required. Check through your coupon collection to see if you have anything that is useful.

- Shop by yourself; don't shop if you are tired because you won't have the energy to shop carefully. Shop after you've eaten—when you're hungry, everything looks good, especially high-energy, nutrient poor "instant" foods.

- Specials (and coupons) for items that you never use are no bargains. However, specials on items you *do* use are a great chance to stock up.

- It is often cheaper to buy whole poultry and cut it up yourself. If you are planning to make soups and stews and utility poultry is available, consider using this less expensive meat.

- Bulk purchases of herbs, pasta and dried fruits are less expensive than buying them pre-packaged (and you only buy as much as you need). The same goes for juices that can be purchased in large containers and then transferred to reusable, single-serving containers and packed for lunch. You can save money and cut down on packaging and waste!

- The more highly processed the item, the more expensive it will be. If there is time to do the preparation (often it only takes a few minutes), you can save money. Meals can be prepared ahead for those days when time is short. You will not only save money but also eat less salt and fat.

Ingredient Know-How

- Powdered vs Salted Herbs and Spices—When shopping for herbs and spices, be sure to buy the powder rather than salt. This applies to garlic and onion powder and celery flavouring. It's an easy way to avoid adding salt when you add flavour.

- Vegetable oil sprays—We have suggested the use of vegetable oil cooking spray in several recipes. Although the cost may seem high, a can of spray lasts a long time and it does a good job. If you prefer, lightly brush vegetable oil on the surface of your baking dishes.

- Margarine—Soft tub margarine is used often in these recipes. It means the margarine is soft enough to spread as soon as it comes out of the fridge. This type of margarine usually has less saturated fat (the fat we want to eat less of).

- Salt—Few of the recipes in this book suggest adding salt. If you find them bland, add a tiny sprinkle after cooking rather than during cooking, or try other spices such as one of the salt-free herb seasoning mixes.

By having the following ingredients on hand you can make almost any recipe in this book. Most of the ingredients are common and are used in many of the recipes.

On the pantry shelf:

all-purpose flour; baking powder; beef bouillon cubes; canned fish such as tuna, sardines, clams or crabmeat; cornstarch; macaroni; light mayonnaise; rice; skim milk powder; prepared mustard; low-sodium soy sauce; granulated white sugar; canned tomatoes; vegetable oil; vinegar; Worcestershire sauce

Seasonings:

(best bought in small amounts at the bulk food store)

bay leaves; curry; dried oregano; dried parsley; dried tarragon; dried thyme; garlic powder; ginger; pepper

Vegetables and Fruit:

apples; cabbage; carrots; celery; onions; potatoes; spinach

In the refrigerator:

skim milk mozzarella cheese; soft margarine; plain lower-fat yogurt

Good to have in the freezer:

chicken pieces; ground beef, pork or chicken; fish fillets

SOUPS AND SAUCES

- To make a simple chicken broth for soups and sauces, save up chicken bones and skin in your freezer until you have time to make it. For a low-salt and low-fat broth, put bones and skin into a saucepan and just cover with water. Bring to a boil and then simmer for 15 minutes. Pour the broth into a sieve, strain into a bowl and refrigerate until the fat solidifies and can be removed.

- To make a simple vegetable broth, chop celery (with leaves), leeks, carrots, onions, zucchini or parsley (or any combination, depending on what's on hand) and simmer in water for an hour. Include a bay leaf, a pinch of garlic powder, some pepper or a teaspoon (5 mL) of dried thyme (if you have it) for flavouring. Strain the liquid and store in the refrigerator for use within four days or freeze the broth for future use.

- Clear soups of broth, small amounts of lean meat, or small pasta shells and/or chopped vegetables can make a satisfying first course or lunch. Puréed soups can be made by cooking vegetables such as carrots, tomatoes, sweet red peppers or spinach in broth and then puréeing them in a blender. For heartier soups, chop meat and vegetables into large pieces and include pasta or legumes, cooking them according to package directions. The soups can be simply seasoned with pepper, onion, garlic powder or a bay leaf.

Country Potato Soup

This recipe came from Manitoba. Small amounts of other vegetables such as finely chopped green peppers, celery or cabbage may be cooked with the potatoes for a variation.

2 cups	water	500 mL
3 cups	thinly sliced peeled potato	750 mL
¾ cup	thinly sliced onion	175 mL
1 tsp	dried parsley	5 mL
1 cup	skim milk	250 mL
1 tbsp	all-purpose flour	15 mL
1 tbsp	soft margarine	15 mL
	Pepper to taste	

In a large pot, heat water to boiling. Add potato, onion and parsley. Return liquid to a boil. Reduce heat and simmer 10 minutes or until potatoes are tender.

Mix together milk, flour, margarine and pepper. Pour into simmering potatoes, gently lifting them so milk can run underneath. Stir soup gently, without breaking potatoes, so that milk heats evenly and lumps don't form. Return to boil.

Remove from heat. Serve immediately.

Makes 2 main-course (1½ cup/375 mL) or 4 appetizer (¾ cup/ 175 mL) servings.

Corn 'n' Crab Chowder

In the west, this rich, thick chowder is made with bacon. If you use bacon, use one slice of back or peameal bacon, browning it well and draining off all fat before chopping it and adding in place of crab. The fat in strip bacon makes it an unwise choice if you are watching fat intake. Although back or peameal bacon is slightly more expensive, it is all lean meat— a much better buy for your budget. Ask your grocery store to package one or two slices for you.

1	medium onion, chopped	1
1 tbsp	vegetable oil	15 mL
1	large potato, peeled and diced	1
1 cup	water	250 mL
1 cup	skim milk	250 mL
½ cup	White Sauce Mix (page 16)	125 mL
1	can (7¾ oz/228 mL) cream-style corn	1
	Pepper to taste	
1	can (7 oz/213 g) crabmeat, well drained	1

In a saucepan, brown onion in oil. Add potato and water. Cook over medium heat 10 to 15 minutes or until potatoes are tender.

In small saucepan, combine milk and White Sauce Mix. Cook over low heat until thick and smooth, stirring constantly. Add corn and pepper.

Stir corn mixture into potatoes and heat for 5 minutes. Add crab and cook for 5 more minutes or until chowder is heated through.

Makes 4 servings (¾ cup/175 mL each).

Hearty Vegetable Soup
(shown on cover)

This soup freezes well so you can make a batch and freeze leftovers in amounts you would use for one meal. Serve with bread or biscuits.

1	can (19 oz/540 mL) red kidney beans, drained	1
½ cup	chopped onion	125 mL
1	can (28 oz/796 mL) tomatoes	1
2	beef bouillon cubes	2
5 cups	water	1.25 L
	Pepper to taste	
½ tsp	dried thyme	2 mL
1	bay leaf	1
1	can (10 oz/284 mL) low-sodium condensed tomato soup	1
1 cup	chopped celery	250 mL
1	cup corn kernels	250 mL
1 cup	diced potatoes, pot barley or macaroni	250 mL
1 tbsp	dried parsley	15 mL

In a large soup pot, combine beans, onion, tomatoes, bouillon cubes, water, pepper, thyme, bay leaf, tomato soup, celery, corn, potatoes and parsley. Bring to a boil. Reduce heat and simmer 35 to 40 minutes or until vegetables are tender.

Remove bay leaf before serving.

Makes 6 to 8 main-course servings.

Maritime Seafood Chowder

You can make this with just the clams or add any leftover seafood, such as white fish. Often fish counters will sell packages of chowder mix—inexpensive packets of small pieces of fish; if this is available, buy ¼ lb (125 g) and add to the clams.

2	cans (each 6½ oz/213 g) small or minced clams	2
1 cup	finely chopped onion	250 mL
1 cup	finely chopped celery or celery and green pepper	250 mL
2 cups	diced potatoes	500 mL
1½ cups	White Sauce Mix (page 16)	375 mL
4 cups	milk	1 L
½ tsp	granulated sugar	2 mL
	Pepper to taste	

Drain clams, reserving liquid.

In a large saucepan, combine clam juice, onion, celery and potatoes. Add just enough water to cover vegetables; cook over medium heat for 15 minutes or until vegetables are tender.

While vegetables are cooking, combine White Sauce Mix and milk in large kettle or Dutch oven. Cook over low heat until thick and smooth, stirring constantly.

Add clams, undrained vegetables and sugar. Heat through, about 15 minutes. Add pepper and serve.

Makes 4 to 6 main-course servings.

White Sauce Mix

A friend in New Brunswick shared her recipe for this easy mix. Make a batch and keep it handy in the refrigerator. Use it to dress up fish or vegetables or to make super-creamy soups and chowders, without worrying about fat and calories.

2 cups	instant skim milk powder	500 mL
1 cup	all-purpose flour	250 mL
1 cup	soft margarine	250 mL

In a large bowl, combine milk powder and flour. Mix well.

With a pastry blender or two knives, cut in margarine until mixture is in fine crumbs. Or place in a food processor and pulse until in fine crumbs, scraping sides and bottom at least once.

Lightly pack mixture into a large-necked, airtight container and store in a refrigerator. **Use within two months.**

The White Sauce Mix can be used for a variety of dishes. In this book it is used in Corn 'n' Crab Chowder (p. 13), Maritime Seafood Chowder (p. 15), Chicken in Creamy Curry Sauce (p. 37), Scalloped Potatoes with Fish (p. 45), Creamy Tuna Pasta Sauce (p. 51) and Macaroni and Cheese (p. 52).

Medium White Sauce

For a thicker sauce, increase mix to ¾ cup (175 mL); for a
thinner sauce, decrease mix to ¼ cup (50 mL).

½ cup	White Sauce Mix	125 mL
1 cup	cool water	250 mL
	Herbs, spices, pepper (optional)	

In a small saucepan, combine White Sauce Mix, water and any
seasonings (if using).

Cook over low heat, stirring constantly, until smooth, 2 to 5
minutes. Makes about 1 cup (250 mL).

* * *

To make a flavoured sauce, substitute tomato juice, chicken or
beef broth for all or part of the water.

* * *

To top poached fish, substitute the fish-poaching liquid for
some or all of the water and add parsley, chives or dill for
flavour.

* * *

For Fish 'n' Curry, make the Medium White Sauce and season
with curry powder to taste (start with 1 tsp/5 mL). Pour over
poached white fish and steamed mixed vegetables.

SALADS AND DRESSINGS

- Salads are especially good for us and may be teamed with one-dish recipes such as Macaroni and Cheese (p. 52) or a hearty soup like Corn 'n' Crab Chowder (p. 13) for a balanced meal.

- You do not need a lot of expensive ingredients to make a salad. Lettuce and one other vegetable such as a tomato or cucumber; cucumber and grated carrot; or cucumber and onion are good with a nice dressing. Try a new variety of greens like Boston lettuce, leaf lettuce or spinach for a treat.

- Make up a low-calorie and easy dressing using equal amounts of oil, lemon juice, orange juice and water (2 tbsp/25 mL each). Add mustard and pepper with a pinch of salt, if necessary. Finely chopped green onions and herbs such as basil or celery seed can be added to taste.

- When you are cooking pasta shells or macaroni, cook some extra to use the next day in a pasta salad.

- The fat in dressings for pasta salads can also be cut back by using a low-fat mayonnaise or substituting low-fat yogurt for part of the mayonnaise.

- "Fibre boost" your salads with carrots, apple slices, dried fruits, broccoli and cauliflower pieces, green peas, chickpeas or kidney beans.

Bean Sprout Salad

To save money, grow your own bean sprouts. Buy sprouting beans at a health food store and ask for instructions. This is a fun project for kids.

1 lb	bean sprouts	500 g
¾ cup	sliced water chestnuts	175 mL
3	stalks celery, thinly sliced	3
1	bunch green onions, sliced lengthwise	1
1 tbsp	white vinegar	15 mL
1 tbsp	low-sodium soy sauce*	15 mL
2 tbsp	vegetable oil	25 mL
1 tbsp	orange juice	15 mL

In a large bowl, combine sprouts, water chestnuts, celery and green onions.

Mix together vinegar, soy sauce, oil and orange juice. Toss half of dressing with vegetables. Toss with enough of the remaining dressing to suit your taste.

Makes 8 servings, (1 cup/250 mL each).

*It's easy to make low-sodium soy sauce. Just use half the required amount of soy sauce and an equal amount of water.

Cinnamon Grape Salad

A nice refreshing dessert when grape prices are low.

½ cup	plain low-fat yogurt	125 mL
Dash	vanilla	Dash
¼ tsp	cinnamon	1 mL
2 cups	seedless green grapes	500 mL
2 cups	seedless red grapes	500 mL

In a large bowl, combine yogurt, vanilla and cinnamon, mixing well.

Stir in grapes until coated. Cover and refrigerate until chilled.

Makes 8 servings (½ cup/125 mL each).

Green Pea Salad

If you make this recipe with frozen green peas, no cooking is necessary—just rinse them under the tap!

1 tbsp	orange juice	15 mL
1 tbsp	lemon juice	15 mL
2 tsp	vegetable oil	10 mL
½ tsp	prepared mustard	2 mL
¼ cup	chopped water chestnuts	50 mL
1	green onion, chopped	1
2 tbsp	minced chives (optional)	25 mL
2 cups	cooked green peas	500 mL

In a small bowl, whisk together orange juice, lemon juice, oil and mustard. Stir in water chestnuts, onion, and chives (if using).

Pour dressing over peas and mix well. Serve chilled or at room temperature.

Makes 4 servings.

Pasta Apple Salad

Take advantage of apples in season to make this quick and tasty salad. For a creamier salad, add more yogurt.

2 cups	cooked cooled macaroni or other small pasta	500 mL
1	apple, cored and diced	1
1	stalk celery, chopped	1
2 tbsp	raisins (optional)	25 mL
6	whole unsalted peanuts, chopped (optional)	6
½ cup	plain low-fat yogurt	125 mL
1/8 tsp	ginger (or to taste)	0.5 mL

In a bowl, combine macaroni, apple, celery, raisins and peanuts (if using). Add yogurt and stir until coated; sprinkle with ginger to taste.

Makes 4 servings.

Buttermilk Dressing

Very nice served over greens such as lettuce.

⅔ cup	buttermilk	150 mL
2 tsp	prepared mustard	10 mL
1	small onion, minced	1
1 tbsp	chopped parsley	15 mL
	Pepper to taste	

In a small bowl or jar, combine buttermilk, mustard, onion, parsley and pepper. Mix or shake together.

Makes ⅔ cup (150 mL).

Chutney-Yogurt Dressing

A different salad dressing, especially nice when served with apple in a salad of green and white vegetables.

⅔ cup	plain low-fat yogurt	150 mL
2 tbsp	(approx) chutney	25 mL

Combine yogurt and chutney, adding more chutney if a stronger flavour is desired.

Makes 8 servings (2 tbsp/25 mL each).

MEAT DISHES

- When buying ground meat (beef or pork) for casseroles or spaghetti, the best buy is regular ground rather than medium or lean. Cook the meat and drain it thoroughly before adding it to the dish. If the ground meat is to be combined raw with other ingredients—for a meat loaf or hamburgers—then your best choice is the medium or lean ground meat since the fat cannot be drained before making the final product. By choosing ground meat carefully you will get the most meat (and the least fat) for your dollars.

- Cheaper cuts of meat usually have less fat but they are less tender and need to be cooked in ways that tenderize them.

  - Braising, boiling and stewing are ideal ways to cook inexpensive cuts of meat. The slow, moist cooking tenderizes the meat and the liquid will become a flavourful sauce.

  - For braising and stewing, brown the meat first to seal in some juices. Braised meat is cut in fairly large pieces; for stewing, smaller cubes are better. The meat is simmered slowly in a small amount of liquid until it is very tender. During the long cooking time, the flavours will blend with any added herbs, vegetables and the cooking liquid. If the dish is made ahead, the flavours will develop even more.

- Use shoulder cuts of beef, lamb, veal or pork, beef brisket, beef round, beef rump, veal shanks or lamb shanks. Remove any visible fat; more will rise to the top during cooking and can be skimmed off. For ham or corned beef, check the liquid and dilute it if it is too salty. If you use salt fish, soak it in cold water overnight and change the water at least three times before cooking.

- The cooking liquid for your meal can be water, stock, beer, cider, wine, chopped tomatoes or a combination.

- Vegetables such as onions, carrots, celery, leeks and garlic can be chopped and added at the beginning of cooking to flavour the sauce.

- More tender vegetables such as zucchini, peas and corn can be added near the end of cooking time so they will not be overcooked or mushy.

- Herbs such as thyme, bay leaves, rosemary, basil, oregano or savoury can be added, as can spices such as cumin, turmeric, coriander or cinnamon.

- A heavy pot with a lid is best for a slow even heat when the meat is simmered rather than boiled to gently break down fibres. After the meat is cooked, the sauce can be boiled to reduce it or it can be thickened with flour.

- If you buy a roast, watch for lean cuts of beef or pork on sale because, although roasts are expensive, there shouldn't be any waste. A roast can be divided into portions for several meals and stored in the freezer. Package meal-sized portions: thin strips for stir-frys, chunks for stews or casseroles and pieces suitable for broiling or barbecuing.

- Instead of making cream sauces or gravies, use herbs and spices such as lemon pepper, rosemary or bay leaves to flavour the meat while it is cooking.

Boiled Ham Dinner

Our favourite boiled dinner is made with inexpensive picnic ham. If you use a boneless ham in this recipe, you will have more than you need and can use the leftover meat in sandwiches for lunch or in another meal.

2 lb	picnic ham	1 kg
1	large carrot, peeled	1
1	small turnip, peeled	1
1	large stalk celery	1
1	large onion	1
Half	small head of cabbage	Half
2	bay leaves	2
2	large potatoes	2

Remove any visible fat from ham; place in a large pot and cover with water.

Chop carrot, turnip and celery into chunks. Cut onion and cabbage into small wedges. Add along with bay leaves to pot, making sure liquid covers meat and vegetables. Bring to a boil and reduce heat; cover and simmer 30 to 40 minutes or until meat is almost tender.

Peel and quarter potatoes; add to pot and return to boil. Reduce to simmer; cover and cook 20 to 25 minutes or until meat and vegetables are tender.

Slice meat and serve with vegetables on a platter.

Makes 4 servings.

CASSEROLES

- Many casseroles can be made ahead and re-heated for those dinners when no one has time to cook.

- Cook pasta such as macaroni, spaghetti or egg noodles and combine with a tomato, cheese or milk-based sauce.

- If you choose to use a prepared soup instead of making your own white sauce, look for low-sodium varieties in order to keep the salt content low.

- A small amount of meat or fish—ground beef, chopped ham, chicken, tuna or seafood—will easily feed a family when served in a casserole.

- Vegetables such as celery, green peas, corn or chopped tomatoes will add fibre and vitamins.

- Toppings such as low-fat grated cheese, toasted whole wheat bread crumbs or a sprinkling of sesame seeds for a nutty taste will add the finishing touch.

Pork or Chicken Casserole

This no-fat method for cooking meat is popular with families in Europe. You can cook this dish in an electric frying pan or crockpot at the same temperature.

The amount of sauerkraut depends on how much meat you have—here we have used one 14-oz (398 mL) can of sauerkraut for four servings. To reduce the salt content, replace some or all of the sauerkraut with shredded cabbage, or rinse the sauerkraut as I did. If using cabbage or drained sauerkraut be sure to add water so that the meat stays moist during cooking.

4	lean pork chops or boneless skinless chicken pieces	4
1	can (14 oz/398 mL) sauerkraut, rinsed and drained or 2 cups (500 mL) shredded cabbage	1
½ cup	water	125 mL
¼ - ½ cup	granulated sugar (optional)	50 - 125 mL

Trim all fat from pork chops. Place meat or chicken in ovenproof dish or pan. Cover with sauerkraut or cabbage, water, and sugar (if using).

Cover and bake at 325°F (160°C) for 1½ hours or until meat is tender.

Makes 4 servings.

Cabbage Roll Casserole

If you can't have cabbage rolls without sour cream, use a low-fat sour cream or a mixture of half sour cream and half plain yogurt.

1 lb	lean ground pork or beef	500 g
1	onion, chopped	1
	Pepper to taste	
Pinch	garlic powder (or to taste)	Pinch
1 tbsp	Worcestershire sauce	15 mL
1	can (14 oz/398 mL) tomatoes, crushed	1
1 cup	water	250 mL
3 tbsp	uncooked rice	50 mL
3 cups	coarsely shredded cabbage	750 mL
	Grated Parmesan cheese (optional)	

In frying pan, brown meat, stirring to break up. Add onion, pepper, garlic and Worcestershire sauce; cook until golden. Pour off all fat. Stir in tomatoes, water and rice.

Place cabbage in large casserole. Pour meat mixture over cabbage.

Cover and bake at 325°F (160°C) for 1½ hours. Check after one hour and stir in a little water if necessary to keep casserole moist. Sprinkle with Parmesan (if using) for last 5 minutes of cooking.

Makes 4 servings.

Microwave Method:

Crumble meat into a large casserole. Cover and microwave on High power for 4 minutes. Stir to break up meat. Drain off fat. Add onion and cook on High power 2 minutes. Drain off fat again.

Add tomatoes, rice, ½ cup (125 mL) water, pepper, garlic and Worcestershire.

Line separate casserole with cabbage; pour meat mixture over top. Cover and microwave on High power for 5 minutes. Cook at Low (10 percent) power for 25 minutes, rotating dish at least twice during cooking. Top with cheese during last minute if desired.

STIR-FRYS

Stir-frying is quick, easy, and a healthy way to prepare food.

- Stir-frying requires high temperatures, very short cooking times and a nimble cook. The secret is to keep the food moving constantly in a tossing, turning motion rather than the circular stirring that the name might indicate.

- A wok is not essential for stir-frying, but its sloping sides make it easier to toss the contents and keep cooked food off to the side and away from the most intense heat. A heavy frying pan or skillet can do the job, just be sure to keep the food in motion.

- To prepare food for stir-frying, cut foods that require the same cooking time into pieces roughly the same size—cut root vegetables into thin slices or small thin strips; vegetables that cook more quickly can be left in larger pieces. Add them to the hot pan in order, from the longest required cooking time to the shortest. For example, broccoli, carrots and onion take longer to cook than peas, mushrooms or small pieces of meat.

- Stir-frying cooks food at such a high heat that vegetable oil is the best choice for fat. Peanut oil, corn oil or canola oil are the usual choices—butter is not suitable because it burns at high temperatures. Ginger or garlic can be added to the hot oil to flavour it.

- Vegetables can include broccoli florets, carrot, celery, or any variety of peppers, onion, cauliflower, turnip, cabbage, green onion, leeks, mushrooms, green peas or snow peas. Stir-fried vegetables will be crunchy, bright in colour and full of flavour. Make sure that the vegetables are dry; otherwise moisture will splatter when it hits the hot fat.

- Meat can be used sparingly—a stir-fry is a budget stretcher. Choose lean meats such as round steak, boneless pork chops or chicken breasts and remove all visible fat. Because the food is cooked at such a high heat, the meat is quickly seared and there is little shrinkage. Small amounts of seafood like shrimp, scallops or oysters can also be used.

- Season a stir-fry with low-sodium soy sauce, oyster sauce, ginger, garlic, curry powder or a sprinkle of sesame seeds.

- Stir-frys are served immediately with lots of rice or noodles for a satisfying meal that covers three of the four food groups—Vegetables and Fruit, Meat and Alternates and Grains.

- Rice is low in calories, fat and sodium, and it is as versatile as pasta. It is a perfect side dish for stir-frys, as well as a moist meat, fish or poultry dish.

- There are a variety of rices available:

  - Brown rice contains bran and germ, making it higher in fibre and a good source of B-vitamins.

  - Parboiled white rice also retains some of the B-vitamins due to the method of processing.

  - Long-grain rice is the most popular because the grains stay separate and fluffy.

  - Short-grain rice is stubby, almost round in shape. When cooked, it gets sticky and a bit heavy in texture.

- One cup (250 mL) of raw rice will make about three times as much when it is cooked; the quick-cooking varieties (already cooked a bit) will make about twice the quantity you started with.

  - Cooking methods are different for different types of rice:

  - a cup of short-grain brown rice should be covered with 2½ cups (625 mL) of water and brought to a boil, then covered and simmered until most of the water is gone— about 40 to 50 minutes. Let it stand for 10 to 15 minutes before serving.

  - Brown rice is even more delicious if you stir in a few thinly sliced mushrooms, sliced green onion, some chopped parsley or even a diced tomato about 10 minutes before the end of cooking time.

  - To save time, especially when making brown rice, make enough to last several meals. Cooked rice will keep up to a week in the refrigerator if it is tightly covered, or longer if it is frozen.

  - To reheat rice that has been refrigerated, spoon it into a tight mesh strainer and steam over boiling water until hot. To reheat in the microwave, place the rice in a microwaveable dish and sprinkle with 1 tbsp (15 mL) of liquid per cup (250 mL) of rice. Cover with vented plastic wrap and microwave on High power until hot (about 1½ minutes per cup/250 mL. If rice is frozen, allow 2 minutes per cup/250 mL).

Easy Stir-fry

A super low-cost meal that can be served with rice.

½ lb	boneless pork chops or lean beef or chicken	250 g
1	clove garlic, minced	1
1 tbsp	low-sodium soy sauce	15 mL
¼ cup	low-sodium beef bouillon	50 mL
1 tsp	ginger	5 mL
1 tbsp	oyster sauce (optional)	15 mL
1 tsp	cornstarch	5 mL
2 tbsp	vegetable oil	25 mL
1 cup	thinly sliced carrots	250 mL
2 cups	broccoli pieces	500 mL
1	medium onion, chopped	1
½ cup	mushrooms, sliced (optional)	125 mL

Remove any visible fat from pork and cut into ¼ -inch (5 mm) strips approximately 2 inches (5 cm) long.

In a bowl, combine garlic, soy sauce, beef bouillon, ginger, and oyster sauce (if using). Add meat and mix well. Let stand in refrigerator for 30 minutes while preparing vegetables. Drain meat and pat dry, reserving marinade. Mix cornstarch into marinade and set aside.

In a large skillet, pan or wok, heat oil until very hot. Add meat; stir-fry for 2 minutes. Remove meat from pan and set aside.

Add carrots to pan (adding a small amount of oil if necessary); stir-fry for 1 minute. Add broccoli and onion; stir-fry for 2 minutes. Add mushrooms (if using); stir-fry for 1 minute.

Return meat to pan. Add marinade mixture and cook, tossing, until vegetables and meat are glazed. Serve immediately.

Makes 4 servings.

POULTRY

Mustard-Baked Chicken

An easy way to cut down on fat is to take the skin off the chicken. If you do this before cooking then you can put the seasonings right on the chicken and enjoy them.

2 tbsp	prepared mustard	25 mL
1 tbsp	lemon juice	15 mL
1 tsp	dried tarragon	5 mL
1	small clove garlic, minced or pinch garlic powder	1
1	slice whole wheat bread	1
4	skinless chicken breasts	4

Mix mustard, lemon juice, tarragon and garlic. Crumble bread into crumbs.

Lightly oil or spray a baking dish with non-stick vegetable oil cooking spray. Place chicken, meaty side up, in dish. Spread chicken with mustard mixture, then sprinkle with crumbs.

Bake at 350°F (180°C) for 45 to 55 minutes or until chicken is no longer pink inside.

Makes 4 servings.

Crispy Chicken Nuggets

Either remove the meat from the chicken breasts or buy packaged boneless chicken. This may seem expensive, but the nuggets will still cost less if prepared at home than those from a fast food outlet, and our version contains very little fat. The nuggets can be made ahead and stored in the fridge until you're ready to bake them, which makes them handy for working moms (or for parties).

1 lb	boneless skinless chicken breasts,* trimmed of all fat	500 g
1	egg white	1
⅔ cup	seasoned bread crumbs**	175 mL

Cut chicken into 2- × 1-inch (5 × 2.5 cm) chunks to make about 36 pieces.

Whisk egg white in large bowl until foamy. Add chicken and mix gently to coat.

Spread about half the seasoned bread crumbs on waxed paper.

Lay half the chicken on crumbs, pressing lightly; turn once to coat with thin layer of crumbs. Place in single layer on large plate. Repeat with remaining crumb mixture and chicken. Cover with plastic wrap and refrigerate for up to 24 hours.

Lightly spray baking sheet with non-stick vegetable oil cooking spray. Arrange chicken in single layer. Bake at 450°F (230°C) for 15 minutes or until chicken is golden and no longer pink in centre. Serve hot.

Makes about 7 servings.

  *Boneless pork can be substituted for the chicken.

**Make seasoned crumbs with crushed non-sugar cereal flakes or bread crumbs; add garlic powder, salt and pepper for seasoning.

Chicken in Creamy Curry Sauce

Sprinkle this easy chicken dish with raisins, chopped peanuts or sliced banana and serve with hot cooked rice for an East Indian meal.

2 tbsp	soft margarine	25 mL
1½ cups	finely chopped peeled apple	375 mL
½ cup	chopped onion	125 mL
1	clove garlic, minced or pinch garlic powder	1
1½ cups	Medium White Sauce (page 17)	375 mL
2 tsp	(approx) curry powder	10 mL
2 cups	cubed cooked chicken (approx 3 chicken breasts)	500 mL

In a deep skillet or saucepan, melt margarine. Add apple, onion and garlic; cook 5 minutes.

Stir in White Sauce and curry powder, adding more curry powder to taste if desired; heat through.

Add chicken and heat through.

Makes 4 to 6 servings.

Spinach Noodles with Lemon Chicken Miniballs

When buying ground chicken or turkey, ask whether any skin or fat is to be found in the meat. If there is, don't buy it—insist on pure ground meat for a low-fat meal.

1 lb	ground chicken or turkey	500 g
2 tbsp	fine dry bread crumbs	25 mL
¼ tsp	grated lemon rind	1 mL
¼ tsp	dried savoury	1 mL
1 lb	spinach noodles	500 g
2 tsp	cornstarch	10 mL
1 cup	low-sodium chicken bouillon	250 mL
2 tbsp	lemon juice	25 mL
Pinch	pepper	Pinch
3	medium carrots, cut into short thin strips	3
1	medium onion, chopped	1
1	medium apple, cored and chopped	1

Combine chicken or turkey, bread crumbs, lemon rind and savoury; mix well. Form into 1-inch (2.5 cm) balls.

Cook noodles according to package directions. Drain.

Whisk together cornstarch, chicken bouillon, lemon juice and pepper.

In a large non-stick frying pan, brown chicken balls on all sides over medium-high heat, about 3 minutes or until meat is cooked.

Reduce heat; add carrots and onions; cook 3 minutes. Add apple and sauce. Cook, stirring until thickened, about 2 minutes. Toss with noodles.

Makes 4 servings.

FISH

- Fish is ideal for a light, nutritious meal. In some parts of the country, fish may not be easy on the budget, but bargains may still be had when fish is in season.

- When purchasing fish, freshness is important. The less "fishy" the smell, the fresher the fish. The odor should be mild and the flesh should be firm.

- If the fish is frozen, thaw it slowly in the refrigerator to keep it firm and cut down on moisture loss; it is a good idea to cook it before it has thawed completely. Some cooks prefer not to defrost it at all, but then the cooking times must be nearly doubled.

- There are lots of low-fat ways to cook fish. Frying it in fat is not a good idea; alternatives such as poaching, steaming, or using in soups and chowders are quick and easy. Fish is cooked to develop flavour, not to make it tender. If you don't overcook fish, you're in for a treat.

- Fish is either lean or fatty. Dry-heat cooking methods such as broiling, grilling and baking will dry out lean fish such as sole, flounder, turbot, cod, snapper and rockfish, which have 5 percent or less fat. These fish have a mild flavour and firm white flesh and are better poached or steamed.

- Salmon, tuna, smelt, trout and sturgeon are examples of fattier fish and contain from 5 percent to 50 percent fat. Their flesh is less white, richer and has a stronger taste. Because the fat content is higher, they are more likely to keep moist during dry-heat cooking.

- Properly cooked fish is opaque and easily comes away from the bone. Fish cooks in a matter of minutes—a good rule of thumb is to allow 10 minutes of cooking for every inch (2.5 cm) of thickness.

- The most important factors in poaching fish are the type of liquid and its temperature. Fish can be poached in salted water, but you can also use water that has wine or vinegar, herbs and vegetables added. Add chopped onion, carrot and/or celery and herbs such as thyme, parsley and a bay leaf, as well as peppercorns and salt. Start the fish in a cold liquid and bring the liquid to a simmer. At the right heat, the surface of the liquid will barely be moving. Almost all types of fish are suitable for poaching except those very high in fat.

- Steaming is similar to poaching except the fish is cooked over the liquid rather than in it. Steaming is ideal for delicately flavoured fish (or vegetables) because the flavours and nutrients aren't absorbed in the poaching liquid.

- Steamers are inexpensive—large bamboo steamers placed in a frying pan work well. Oil the steamer where it will touch the fish or lay the fish on a lettuce leaf to keep it from sticking. The food cooks best when it is in one layer—if it is a small steamer, steam the food in several one-layer batches. Be sure the water is boiling before you add the food so the steam will sear it and keep juices in. The food should be at least 1 inch (2.5 cm) above the water to make sure that the vigorously bubbling water doesn't boil it. The water can be flavoured with a little vinegar, onion, celery, carrots or herbs and should boil continuously for a constant flow of steam—keep a kettle of hot water ready to top up the supply. It's important not to allow the water to boil dry.

- Fish can also be broiled, grilled or barbecued. These are dry heat methods best for fattier varieties of fish; fillets with the skin left on or steaks work best on a grill. They should be an inch (2.5 cm) or so thick (thin fish may break apart as it cooks). Use a high heat and watch the fish carefully; it cooks fast on the grill. Spray the rack, grill or broiling pan with a non-stick vegetable oil cooking spray or brush it lightly with oil. Brush the fish with oil or a non-fat basting liquid such as tomato juice to keep it moist. Cook over a grill or under the broiler at high heat and turn only once during cooking. Once again, thickness will dictate the cooking time.

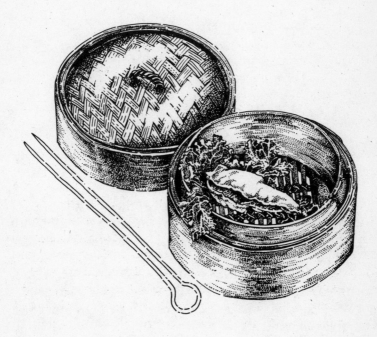

Fish Dinner in Foil

This recipe cooks your whole meal in a packet. If your family works different hours, make up a packet each so that everyone can have a nutritious hot meal when they come home, no matter what their shift. No pots and pans to wash!

  If you want to do this in the microwave instead, use waxed paper instead of foil and microwave one packet at a time on High power for six to eight minutes.

2 tsp	soft margarine	10 mL
½ lb	frozen fish fillets	250 g
	Pepper	
1	small onion, chopped	1
4 tsp	lemon juice	20 mL
2	slices tomato	2
2 tsp	low-fat mayonnaise	10 mL
2	small potatoes, peeled and sliced	2
2	small carrots, sliced	2

Spread margarine on shiny side of two pieces of foil large enough to hold half of the fish and vegetables. (Or spray foil with non-stick vegetable oil cooking spray.)

  On each piece of foil, place fillets. Sprinkle with pepper to taste, onion and lemon juice. Place tomato on fish; dot with mayonnaise.

  Arrange potatoes and carrots around fish.

  Close foil tightly so that no juices can escape. Place on baking sheet or pan. Bake at 400°F (200°C) for 20 to 25 minutes or until fish flakes easily when tested with fork and vegetables are tender.

Makes 2 servings.

Steamed Mussels or Clams

These shellfish make a wonderful meal and are often inexpensive. They should look healthy, not dry and the odour should be mild. Store the shellfish in a cool place and use them the day you buy them. Serve the cooking liquid with bread to dunk in it while you enjoy a feed of mussels or clams.

1 lb	mussels or clams	500 g
¼ cup	water, beer or wine	50 mL
1	each piece (2-inch/5 cm) celery, carrot and onion	1

Rinse shellfish and discard any with broken shells.

Add water, beer or wine to a large pot. Add celery, carrot and onion pieces.

Add mussels or clams; cook over high heat for 4 to 5 minutes, covered, or until shells open and meat is cooked. **Throw away any mussels or clams that do not open when steamed.**

Drain liquid from pot through a sieve, piece of gauze or coffee filter and serve in small bowl.

Makes 1 main course serving or 2 appetizer servings.

Italian Fish

This was how we convinced our son that fish tastes good! He called it pizza fish. For a special treat, cover the fish with grated part-skim milk mozzarella cheese and broil for the last minute or so of cooking, until the cheese melts and begins to brown. Since you have the oven on, why not bake potatoes to serve at the same meal?

1 lb	white fish fillets, frozen	500 g
1 cup	vegetables such as chopped tomato, onion, mushrooms, peppers (hot or sweet), eggplant (peeled) corn niblets, broccoli florets, cauliflower florets, shredded cabbage	250 mL
1	can (10 oz/284 mL) spaghetti sauce	1
¼ cup	grated Parmesan cheese, optional	50 mL

Place fish in a loaf pan and cover with vegetables. Pour spaghetti sauce over top; sprinkle with Parmesan (if using).

Bake at 450°F (230°C) for 20 minutes or until fish flakes easily when tested with a fork.

Makes 4 servings.

Scalloped Potatoes with Fish

A friend from Montreal who grew up in Saskatchewan told me that her family used to eat a lot of scalloped potatoes layered with sardines for a nutritious and filling meal. Use water-packed sardines.

1½ cups	Medium White Sauce (page 17)	375 mL
3	large potatoes, peeled and thinly sliced	3
1 to 2	cans (each 3.5 oz/100 g) sardines, packed in water, drained	1 to 2
	Pepper or paprika (optional)	

In a casserole, layer White Sauce, potatoes and sardines, ending with potatoes, then White Sauce. Sprinkle with pepper or paprika (if using).

Bake at 350°F (180°C) for 20 minutes or until potatoes are tender.

Makes 4 servings.

Tuna Delight

A great way to use up leftover flaked fish and vegetables.
Served on whole grain toast with a tangy cheese sauce, it's a
quick and nutritious meal.

2	slices whole grain toast	2
1 cup	vegetables, such as cooked broccoli florets, mixed vegetables or canned asparagus cuts, drained	250 mL
1	can (4 oz/113 g) water-packed tuna, drained, or equal amount of leftover cooked white fish or salmon	1

Light Cheese Sauce:

2 tbsp	grated part-skim milk mozzarella cheese	25 mL
2 tbsp	low-fat mayonnaise	25 mL
¼ cup	skim milk	50 mL

Light Cheese Sauce:
In a small saucepan, combine cheese, mayonnaise and skim
milk; heat for a few seconds over medium heat, stirring
constantly, until smooth.

Place toast and vegetables on 2 small heatproof plates; top
with tuna, then hot cheese sauce.
    Broil until cheese begins to brown, if desired.

Makes 2 servings.

PASTA DISHES

Pasta is inexpensive and easily-prepared. It is a good source of iron and B-vitamins. Top it with a sauce of your own invention and you've got a quick and satisfying meal. Pasta itself is not a source of fat—it's the toppings that do the damage. Find ways of cutting back on the fat in your recipes and you're on your way to Heart Smart eating.

- Use lean meats in your sauces. Consider regular ground beef or pork (or substitute a can of clams) for your spaghetti sauce (be sure to drain it well), use lean beef for stews, and look for recipes that use chicken or water-packed tuna instead of high-fat sausage or bacon. When the meat must be cooked first, do so in a small amount of vegetable oil or water to keep it from sticking.

- Slim down the sauces by substituting lower-fat milk for cream and add flavour with herbs, spices and vegetables instead of relying on heavy cream to make the sauce special.

- Top dishes with a sprinkle of sesame seeds, whole wheat bread crumbs or a low-fat grated cheese.

- When cooking pasta, remember salted water is not necessary but it is important to use lots of water. Cooking times will vary with the size and shape of the pasta and it is best to follow the manufacturer's instructions for cooking it. Test the pasta to make sure it's at the preferred texture; it should be tender yet firm. Fresh pasta will cook in less time than dried. Always drain it thoroughly and serve immediately.

- To save time, cook a double batch of pasta such as macaroni and use the extra for a salad the next day.

Oven-Baked Lasagna

Lasagna is very nutritious and low in fat and calories when low-fat ingredients are used. Serve with a tossed salad. This recipe calls for spinach, but I've also made it with chopped broccoli.

If you use oven-ready lasagna noodles, you do not need to cook them first. However when you place them in your casserole, leave space between the noodles so they can expand.

4 to 6	lasagna noodles	4 to 6
1 lb	lean ground beef or pork	500 g
¼ tsp	dried oregano	1 mL
2 cups	tomato or spaghetti sauce	500 mL
1 cup	low-fat cottage cheese	250 mL
1	package (10 oz/300 g) frozen spinach, thawed and drained, or (10 oz/284 mL) fresh	1
1	package (6 oz/170 g) skim milk mozzarella cheese, sliced or grated	1

Cook noodles according to package directions.

In a frying pan, brown meat, stirring to break up; drain off all fat.

Add oregano to tomato or spaghetti sauce.

Spray a 9-inch (2.5 L) square pan with non-stick vegetable oil cooking spray.

Make layers using half each of noodles, then cottage cheese, meat, spinach, mozzarella and tomato sauce. Repeat.

Bake at 350°F (180°C) for 30 minutes. Let sit 5 to 10 minutes before serving.

Makes 4 to 6 servings.

Microwave Spinach Lasagna

Lasagna does not need meat to make it good!

4 to 6	lasagna noodles	4 to 6
2 cups	skim milk ricotta cheese	500 mL
1	package (10 oz/300 g) frozen chopped spinach, thawed and drained	1
2 cups	tomato or spaghetti sauce	500 mL
6	slices skim milk mozzarella cheese	6
¼ cup	grated Parmesan cheese (optional)	50 mL

Cook noodles according to package directions.

Mix ricotta with chopped spinach.

In a 9-inch (2.5 L) square microwaveable casserole, layer ½ cup (125 mL) sauce, half of the noodles, half the ricotta mixture, 3 slices mozzarella, ½ cup (125 mL) sauce. Repeat.

Cover with vented plastic wrap and microwave on High power 15 minutes, rotating dish once during cooking.

Sprinkle with Parmesan (if using). Microwave, uncovered, on Medium (50 percent) power for 10 minutes. Let stand 5 minutes before serving.

Makes 4 servings.

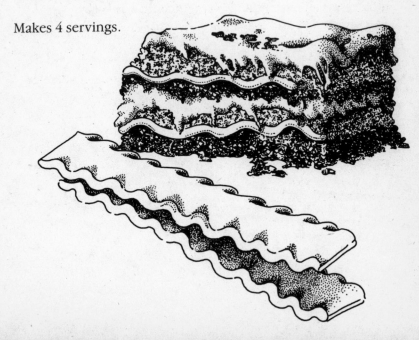

Microwave Clams and Pasta

Simple to prepare. Yummy to eat. The parsley can be grown
on your windowsill, in your garden, purchased when cheap,
or to save money, snip the centre leaves from celery.

8 oz	spaghettini	250 g
2 tsp	vegetable oil	10 mL
½ cup	minced green onions	125 mL
2	cloves garlic, finely chopped	2
½ cup	snipped fresh parsley	125 mL
1	can (10 oz/284 mL) baby clams, with liquid	1
1	can (10 oz/284 mL) sliced mushrooms, drained	1
¼ cup	grated Parmesan cheese	50 mL

Cook spaghettini according to package directions, being
careful not to overcook. Drain, saving ¼ cup (50 mL) of the
water.

Meanwhile, in a large microwaveable bowl, combine oil,
onions, garlic, parsley and clam juice. Cover and microwave
on High for 5 minutes. Stir.

Add reserved pasta water, pasta, mushrooms, clams,
Parmesan cheese and toss well.

Serve immediately.

Makes 4 servings.

Creamy Tuna Sauce for Pasta

Serve this light sauce over your favourite noodles (or have it on whole wheat toast). Add a sprinkle of dried dillweed or a little grated lemon rind. Vegetables can include peas, chopped carrot, broccoli or onion.

1	can (7.2 oz/180 g) water-packed tuna, drained	1
1 cup	cooked vegetables	250 mL
Pinch	each dried dillweed and	Pinch
	grated lemon rind (optional)	
2 cups	Medium White Sauce (page 17)	500 mL

Add tuna, vegetables, and dill and lemon (if using) to Medium White Sauce. Heat through.

Makes 3 cups (750 mL).

Macaroni and Cheese

To cut down on the fat in this dish, try mixing low-fat
Cheddar or part skim-milk mozzarella with a small amount of
extra-old Cheddar or your family's favourite cheese. Even
with low-fat cheese, this recipe is still high in fat. Serve it with
chopped vegetables and fruit salad for a balanced meal.

You can also add zest to a low-fat cheese sauce by adding a
little more Worcestershire and mustard and a sprinkling of
Parmesan cheese on top with the bread crumbs (or add a
pinch of cayenne pepper).

1½ cups	macaroni	375 mL
1½ cups	Medium White Sauce (page 17)	375 mL
1 tsp	Worcestershire sauce	5 mL
½ tsp	dry mustard	2 mL
1 to 1½ cups	grated low-fat hard cheese	250 to 375 mL
¼ cup	toasted whole grain bread crumbs	50 mL
2 tbsp	grated cheese	25 mL

Cook macaroni according to package directions.

Combine White Sauce, Worcestershire sauce and mustard;
stir in cheese until melted.

Lightly grease or spray an 8-inch (2 L) casserole with
vegetable oil cooking spray. Add macaroni and cheese sauce
and mix well; top with toasted bread crumbs. Sprinkle grated
cheese on top.

Bake at 400°F (200°C) for 15 to 20 minutes or until bubbly
and crusty.

Makes 4 servings.

VEGETABLES

- Green beans and peas are very good sources of fibre and quite inexpensive. Add them to whatever you can—chowders, soups, casseroles, stir-fry meals, salads, rice or noodles.

- Choose fresh vegetables when they are in season. The nutritional value and price will be best at that time. Storage and preparation methods are very important when purchasing fresh produce. Do not wash or trim the produce before you put it away. It is best to do this right before you use it. Cook the vegetables in as small amount of liquid as possible—microwaving is a great method for cooking vegetables.

- Frozen vegetables are a great alternative to fresh. The vegetables are picked and frozen at the prime of the season. Keep vegetables frozen until you're ready to use them.

- Canned vegetables can be cheaper to use than fresh or frozen at certain times of the year. During processing, salt is usually added and some of the nutrients are lost. It is best not to use canned vegetables as your only source of vegetables.

Potatoes

Be sure to include potatoes on your grocery list—almost everyone loves them and they are easy on the budget.

- There are only 100 calories in a medium-sized potato. When eaten by themselves, they are nutritious and fat-free. They are best cooked whole and eating the skins will give you extra fibre.

- Instead of high-fat toppings such as butter, margarine, sour cream or a rich cheese sauce, try dressing up your potatoes with low-fat yogurt, either plain or mixed with chopped green onion or herbs such as parsley or chives; mock sour cream, made by blending low-fat cottage cheese with lemon juice; low-fat sour cream; leftover vegetables, alone or in combination with the yogurt or mock sour cream; salsa; or Light Cheese Sauce (see page 46).

- Potatoes can be baked at temperatures between 325°F and 425°F (160°C and 220°C) so they can always be baked when the oven is on for something else. (A metal skewer or prong pushed into the centre of the potato will make it cook faster.) Long potatoes are best for baking or microwaving. Round ones are best boiled.

Oven-Baked Potatoes:

Wash potatoes and prick skins several times with a fork.

Place on the oven rack around whatever else is cooking, allowing for the following times for medium-sized potatoes.

425°F (220°C): 40-50 minutes

375°F (190°C): 50-60 minutes

325°F (160°C): 75-85 minutes

When a knife goes easily to the centre, potatoes are cooked. Cut a cross in the top and press to let the steam out before you serve them.

Microwave Method:

Be sure to use potatoes that are the same size.

Wash, pat dry and prick with a fork. One potato: place in the centre of the microwave oven on a double layer of paper towelling. Two or more potatoes: lay potatoes on a double thickness of paper towelling in a spoke pattern.

Cooking time depends on the number of potatoes, their size and your microwave oven. Check your manual for instructions. As a guide, four large baking potatoes (about 8 oz/250 g each) will take 10 to 15 minutes at High in a 750-watt microwave oven. Turn the potatoes over halfway through baking time. Wrap the potatoes in paper towels if you need to absorb any moisture. Allow to stand 5 minutes before testing for doneness as they will continue cooking after the microwave stops.

Easy Vegetable Pie

A great way to use up leftover vegetables such as cooked cauliflower, carrots, broccoli, green beans, raw zucchini or raw or drained canned tomatoes.

2 cups	chopped vegetables	500 mL
2 tbsp	chopped onion	25 mL
¼ cup	grated low-fat cheese	50 mL
1	egg, beaten	1
¼ cup	Easy Scone and Biscuit Mix (page 57)	50 mL
½ cup	skim milk	125 mL
	Pepper	

Spray deep 10-inch (25 cm) pie plate with non-stick vegetable oil cooking spray.

In a bowl, mix chopped vegetables, onion and cheese; spread in pie plate.

In another bowl, combine beaten egg, Biscuit Mix, milk, and pepper to taste. Pour over vegetable mixture.

Bake at 400°F (200°C) for 30 to 35 minutes or until a knife inserted comes out clean. Let stand 5 minutes before cutting and serving.

Makes 8 servings.

BAKING

Easy Scone and Biscuit Mix

This mix can be made in bulk and stored in a cool dry place for up to a month. It is low in cost and can be used in a variety of ways.

4 cups	all-purpose flour	1 L
1½ cups	instant skim milk powder	375 mL
7½ tsp	baking powder	37 mL
1½ tsp	salt	7 mL
2 tbsp	granulated sugar	25 mL
¾ cup	vegetable oil	175 mL

Mix flour, skim milk powder, baking powder, salt and sugar thoroughly.

Add vegetable oil and mix until crumbly.

Store in a tightly covered glass or plastic container in a cool place (it is not necessary to refrigerate it) for **use within one month**.

Makes 7 cups (1.75 L).

Tea Biscuits

4 cups	Easy Scone and Biscuit Mix (p. 57)	1 L
¾ cup	cold water	175 mL

Combine Easy Scone and Biscuit Mix and water until mixture forms stiff dough.

Turn dough onto lightly floured surface and knead until no longer sticky, sprinkling with more flour if necessary.

Roll or pat to ½-inch (1 cm) thickness. Cut out rounds with 2-inch (5 cm) cookie cutter or drinking glass. Place on ungreased cookie sheet or baking pan.

Bake at 425°F (220°C) until golden, about 15 minutes. Remove from pan while still warm.

Makes 12 to 18 biscuits.

Variations:

Drop Tea Biscuits: Increase water to 1¼ cups (300 mL) to make a soft dough that can be dropped from a tablespoon. Dough will be sticky. Do not knead or cut rounds. Bake at 425°F (220°C) until slightly browned, about 20 minutes. Makes 18 to 20 biscuits.

Cheese Tea Biscuits: Add ¼ cup (50 mL) shredded Parmesan or ½ to ¾ cup (125 to 175 mL) of sharp Cheddar cheese to Tea Biscuit recipe. Proceed as in Tea Biscuit recipe.

Savoury Cheese Tea Biscuits: Add 3 tbsp (50 mL) minced onion and ½ cup (125 mL) finely chopped green or red sweet pepper to Cheese Tea Biscuit recipe. Proceed as in Tea Biscuit recipe.

Orange Tea Biscuits: Add 4 tsp (20 mL) granulated sugar to Tea Biscuit recipe. Substitute 1 tbsp (15 mL) orange juice for part of the water and add 1 tbsp (15 mL) grated orange rind. Proceed as in Tea Biscuit recipe.

Cinnamon Drops: Add ¼ cup (50 mL) granulated sugar and 1 tsp (5 mL) cinnamon to Tea Biscuit recipe. Mix and knead dough as above. Form dough into balls instead of cutting into rounds. Combine ¼ cup (50 mL) granulated sugar and 1 tsp (5 mL) cinnamon on a plate and roll balls in the mixture, coating them completely. Place on a lightly greased cookie sheet and bake at 350°F (180°C) for 10 to 12 minutes.

Easy Scones

3 cups	Easy Scone and Biscuit Mix (p. 57)	750 mL
¼ cup	granulated sugar	50 mL
⅓ cup	raisins	75 mL
¾ tsp	baking powder	4 mL
2 tbsp	vegetable oil	25 mL
1	egg, beaten	1
½ cup	skim milk	125 mL
1 tsp	vanilla	5 mL

Coat baking sheet with non-stick vegetable oil cooking spray or grease lightly.

In a bowl, combine Scone and Biscuit Mix, sugar, raisins and baking powder.

Combine oil, egg, milk and vanilla; mix into dry ingredients to make a soft dough, adding extra milk if necessary.

Turn out onto lightly floured surface. Knead until smooth and not sticky.

Pat or roll dough out to about ½ -inch (1 cm) thickness. Cut into squares or rounds and place on baking sheet.

Bake at 375°F (190°C) 15 to 20 minutes or until lightly browned.

Makes 12 to 18 scones.

Easy Pancakes

Serve these topped with syrup, applesauce, yogurt or jam.

1 cup	Easy Scone and Biscuit Mix (p. 57)	250 mL
¾ cup	water	175 mL
1	egg, beaten	1

Beat Scone and Biscuit Mix, water and egg together until smooth.

Lightly grease large frying pan. Pour batter into hot frying pan or drop by tablespoonfuls (15 mL) for smaller pancakes. Cook until edges dry slightly and bubbles appear. Turn once, cooking until golden brown.

Makes 10 to 12 4-inch (10 cm) pancakes.

Easy Dumplings

1¼ cups	Easy Scone and Biscuit Mix (p. 57)	300 mL
½ cup	water	125 mL

Combine Scone and Biscuit Mix and water to make soft dough.

Drop by spoonfuls on top of soups or stews. Cover and continue cooking for 15 to 20 minutes or until dumplings are cooked. Do not remove cover while cooking.

Makes 10 to 12 dumplings.

Cranberry Bran Muffins

Best served warm. Excellent for breakfast or TV snacks.

2 cups	bran cereal (not flakes)	500 mL
1½ cups	skim milk	375 mL
1 cup	cranberries, finely chopped	250 mL
2 tbsp	granulated sugar	25 mL
2 cups	all-purpose flour	500 mL
1 tbsp	baking powder	15 mL
1/8 tsp	salt (optional)	0.5 mL
¼ cup	honey	50 mL
2 tbsp	vegetable oil	25 mL
1	egg, beaten	1
1½ tsp	vanilla	7 mL

Spray 12 muffin tins with non-stick vegetable oil cooking spray or grease lightly.

In a large bowl, mix cereal and milk together. Let stand 10 minutes, stirring several times.

In another bowl, mix cranberries and sugar; set aside.

In third bowl, sift flour, baking powder, and salt (if using).

Stir honey, oil, egg, vanilla and cranberry mixture into cereal. Add dry ingredients and stir just until moistened.

Spoon batter into muffin cups, dividing evenly. Bake at 400°F (200°C) for about 20 minutes or until muffins spring back when pressed lightly.

Makes 12 muffins.

DESSERTS

Popovers

Here's a low-fat, "can't fail" popover recipe that we can enjoy without guilt. It teams well with honey and strawberries or jam. A little grated orange rind and nutmeg can be added to the batter.

Glass custard cups are best for baking popovers, or use muffin pans. Be sure the oven is hot. Cook when you are using the oven for something else to save energy.

6	egg whites*	6
1 cup	skim milk	250 mL
2 tbsp	soft margarine, melted	25 mL
1 cup	all-purpose flour	250 mL
¼ tsp	salt	1 mL

Spray muffin tins or custard cups with non-stick vegetable oil cooking spray.

Beat egg whites until foamy; add milk and margarine. Beat at medium speed until well blended. Gradually add flour and salt, beating until smooth.

Pour batter into muffin tins or custard cups, filling three-quarters full.

Bake at 375°F (190°C) for 50 minutes, then cut small slit in top of each popover and cook for 5 more minutes. Serve immediately.

Makes 12 popovers.

*Leftover egg yolks can be frozen for later use. If the frozen yolks will be used in a savoury dish, add ½ tsp (2 mL) salt for every ¼ cup (50 mL) of egg yolk (3 eggs); if they will be used in a sweet dish, add 1 tsp (5 mL) sugar for every ¼ cup (50 mL) of yolk.

Whipped Skim Milk Topping

Try this easy topping (and the next one) on fruit desserts.

¼ cup	cold water	50 mL
1½ tsp	lemon juice	7 mL
⅓ cup	instant skim milk powder	75 mL
Few grains	salt	Few grains
4 tsp	granulated sugar	20 mL
Dash	vanilla	Dash

In a bowl, combine water, lemon juice, skim milk powder and salt. Beat until frothy, about 5 minutes.
    Gradually beat in sugar, then vanilla.
    Chill and use within 1 hour.

Makes 1 cup (250 mL).

Yogurt Topping

1 cup	low-fat plain yogurt	250 mL
1 to 2 tbsp	brown sugar	15 to 25 mL
½ tsp	vanilla	2 mL

Combine yogurt, brown sugar and vanilla, adding more brown sugar to taste.

Makes 1 cup (250 mL).

Strawberry Delight Sherbet

You can make this frozen yogurt dessert with almost any kind of fruit—blueberries are also good. It needs to be frozen twice to keep the mixture from separating.

2 cups	fresh strawberries, washed and hulled	500 mL
½ cup	granulated sugar	125 mL
1½ cups	plain yogurt	325 mL

In a bowl, beat together strawberries and sugar for 2 minutes. Blend in yogurt. Pour into 9-inch (2.5 L) square pan.

Freeze mixture until solid, about 2 hours. Break into chunks in a large chilled bowl; beat for 5 minutes. Spoon into 4 cup (1 L) mould for a fancy dessert or use ice cream or yogurt container to keep for longer period. Cover and freeze overnight.

Makes 3½ cups (875 mL).

Pineapple Sherbet

To make this sherbet you need a blender or food processor. If you don't have one, use a nut chopper for a coarser frozen dessert, but work quickly or it will thaw.

This can also be made with fresh pineapple—peel and core a medium-sized pineapple, cut into chunks and freeze. Substitute ½ cup (125 mL) skim milk for juice.

1	can (20 oz/600 mL) pineapple chunks, packed in its own juice	1

Drain pineapple, reserving ½ cup (125 mL) juice. Freeze pineapple until firm, about 1 hour.

Place frozen chunks in blender along with reserved juice; process until smooth. Serve at once, or return to freezer to eat any time.

Makes 4 servings.

Honey Banana Yogurt

Honey yogurt is good with any type of fruit. Mix and match your favourites when they're in season.

	Honey	
2 cups	low-fat yogurt	500 mL
2	medium-sized ripe bananas	2
	Cinnamon	

Stir honey to taste into yogurt. Slice bananas and add to yogurt. Sprinkle with cinnamon to taste.

Makes 4 servings.

Hot Ginger Orange

This tangy treat can be eaten alone or spooned over frozen yogurt. You can substitute pineapple or grapefruit for the orange.

1	orange, peeled and cut in chunks	1
1 tbsp	brown sugar	15 mL
	Ginger	

Place orange chunks in two small heatproof dishes. Sprinkle with brown sugar, and ginger to taste.
   Broil 5 to 6 minutes or until hot. Serve immediately.

Makes 2 servings.

Fruit Crisp

Make a quick baked dessert with your favourite fruit—apples, peaches, strawberries, blueberries or try a combination. Use either canned or fresh fruit or thaw frozen fruit and drain. Choose cinnamon or lemon rind or juice to flavour most crisps. Top the crisp with Whipped Skim Milk Topping or Yogurt Topping (page 64).

3 cups	sliced fruit	750 mL
1 to 2 tbsp	granulated sugar	15 to 25 mL
½ tsp	cinnamon (optional)	2 mL
½ cup	rolled oats	125 mL
½ cup	brown sugar	125 mL
¼ cup	all-purpose flour	50 mL
¼ cup	margarine	50 mL

Lightly grease an 8- or 9-inch (2 or 2.5 L) square baking dish. Drain canned fruit or wash, peel or slice fresh fruit as appropriate. Spread in baking dish; sprinkle with granulated sugar, and cinnamon (if using).

In a bowl, combine rolled oats, brown sugar, and flour. Cut in margarine until mixture resembles coarse crumbs. Sprinkle over fruit.

Bake at 350°F (180°C) for 30 to 35 minutes or until fruit is bubbly and tender and topping browned.

Makes 4 to 6 servings.

BREAKFAST

- Start your day with a fibre-rich cereal. Oatmeal, bran flakes, oat bran, wheat flakes and shredded wheat are all good for you, and these plain cereals cost less than sugar-coated brands. If you (or your family) can't give up the sweetened cereals, try substituting half with a plain cereal.

- Liven up plain cereals by topping them with a spoonful of raisins, a sliced banana or berries.

- A carefully planned breakfast will include a number of choices from the four food groups and get you started on your quota for the day. A breakfast of juice, cereal with lower-fat milk and toast contains 1 fruit serving, 2 from the grains group and at least half a serving of milk. If you add fruit to the cereal, perhaps a little cheese on your toast and ½ cup (125 mL) of milk to drink, you're even further ahead.

- If you don't want to spend a lot of time on breakfast, consider a blender drink with fruit, milk, yogurt and honey or wheat germ added. There are also all kinds of non-traditional foods that you may prefer for breakfast, like some of the fruit and yogurt dips, a toasted sandwich like Sardine Surprise (page 76) or a Mackerel Sandwich (page 74). Let your taste buds and the food groups be your guide.

- Check out these recipes for more delicious breakfast treats. Serve the following with Prune Apple Butter (page 86) or Honey Nut Spread (page 87) rather than butter or margarine:

Cranberry Bran Muffins (page 62)

Cinnamon Drops (page 59)

Cheese or Orange Tea Biscuits (page 58-9)

Easy Pancakes (page 61)

Granola

Store-bought granola can be expensive and also very high in sugars and fats. If you make your own, you can reduce the cost and control the sugar and fat. This quick-to-make recipe can serve as the base to which you can add wheat germ, sunflower seeds, chopped nuts or dried fruit.

3 tbsp	soft margarine	50 mL
¼ cup	brown sugar or honey	50 mL
¼ cup	water	50 mL
2½ cups	regular rolled oats (not quick-cooking)	625 mL
½ cup	bran cereal	125 mL

In a saucepan, blend margarine, brown sugar and water; heat until sugar has dissolved. Cool slightly.

Pour over oats and bran in a shallow baking dish. Toss to blend and spread about ¼ inch (5 mm) thick.

Bake at 350°F (180°C) for 15 to 20 minutes or until golden, stirring once or twice. Cool and store in airtight container for up to 6 months.

Makes 3 cups (750 mL).

Apple Raisin Triangles

If you don't have raisin bread, try this on whole wheat bread and add a sprinkle of raisins before you put the applesauce on top.

1	slice raisin bread	1
2 tbsp	applesauce	25 mL
	Cinnamon	

Toast raisin bread. Spread with applesauce. Sprinkle with cinnamon to taste. Broil until bubbly. Cut into triangles to serve.

Makes 1 serving.

LUNCHES AND SNACKS

- A brown-bag lunch is cheaper and healthier than one from the local fast-food outlet. Pack a salad, muffin, fresh fruit or yogurt. Use whole wheat pita, whole grain or bran breads for sandwiches. Peanut butter and banana, cucumber and tomato, or sardines are good fillers.

- Cooked roast beef or pork is a smart alternative to luncheon meats. The meat has lower fat, lower salt and lower cost than prepared meats. Slice it thinly and season with different mustards, horseradish, ketchup or light mayonnaise as a spread. Pack lettuce, sprouts, tomato or onion separately to add crisp garnishes to your lunchtime sandwich.

- Have pasta with a low-fat, meatless tomato sauce for lunch, or make a meal out of split-pea soup and a whole wheat bun.

- Hot herb bread is better for you than garlic bread loaded with cheese. Use a sliced loaf of day-old bread and spread with margarine, then sprinkle with parsley, oregano, dill and perhaps Parmesan. Either toast the slices under the broiler or re-assemble the loaf, wrap it in foil and bake at 400°F (200°C) for 10 minutes.

- Light snack ideas include fresh fruits, raw vegetables with dip, low-fat cheese (skim or part-skim mozzarella or farmer's) and pita crisps, unbuttered popcorn or low-fat yogurt with fruit. All are good sources of fibre as well.

- Snack on bread sticks or a whole wheat bun to fill yourself up without adding extra fat.

Mackerel Sandwich Filling

Spread on toast for open-faced sandwiches or use as a filling for whole grain bread slices or in pitas. This filling is also good when made with tuna. Both are strongly flavoured fish, so a little of the filling goes a long way.

1	can (14 oz/398 mL) mackerel, drained	1
¼ cup	chili sauce	50 mL
¼ tsp	garlic powder	1 mL
2 tsp	lemon juice	10 mL

Remove skin from mackerel and flake. Combine with chili sauce, garlic powder and lemon juice, mixing well.

Makes 6 servings.

Franny's Fish Sandwich

Tuna and salmon are sandwich favourites, but often other fish and shellfish are just as delicious and more economical. All work well in sandwiches or as stuffing for pitas. Try canned mackerel, sardines or shellfish such as crab. Leftover cooked, flaked fish is also very good.

1	can (6½ oz/184 g) water-packed tuna, salmon or other flaked cooked fish	1
½ cup	low-fat cottage cheese, mashed	125 mL
3 tbsp	finely chopped celery	50 mL
2 tbsp	finely chopped green onion	25 mL
4	pitas or bread for 4 sandwiches	4
	Sliced tomato	
	Shredded lettuce or alfalfa sprouts	

Drain and flake fish. Combine with cottage cheese, celery and onion.

Fill pitas or build sandwiches with fish mixture, tomato slices, shredded lettuce or sprouts.

Makes 4 servings.

Sardine Surprise

We call this a surprise because we were surprised to learn that Canadians team sardines with so many different things. Select water-packed sardines. These open-faced sandwiches are one suggestion for enjoying this inexpensive fish; do try inventing your own.

2	slices bread	2
1	can (3.5 oz/100 g) water-packed sardines	1
	Pepper	

Group I:
1 tsp (5 mL) or less of:
    Mustard or Malt Vinegar or Ketchup or
    Light Mayonnaise or Low-fat Sour Cream

Group II:
    Thinly sliced cucumber
    Sliced tomato
    Sliced pickle
    Shredded lettuce
    Alfalfa sprouts

Toast bread. Drain sardines and mash. Mix with one selection from Group I.

Place selected garnishes (Group II) on toast and top with sardine mixture. Sprinkle with pepper to taste.

Cut into quarters.

Makes 1 serving.

PIZZA

Save money and make your own pizza in less time than it takes to have one delivered. As well, you will be able to reduce the fat.

Pizza crust:

Pick up ready-made pizza crusts at your supermarket or buy fresh or frozen pizza dough, ready to be rolled out. Frozen bread dough can also be used—simply thaw it and divide it in half. Flatten into rounds about ½ inch (1 cm) thick and pinch edge to make ridge. Brush with vegetable oil.

Alternate pizza crusts include English muffins, pita bread or bagels, all of which can be split in half to make individual pizzas. People can then build their own custom pizza from the available toppings.

You can also make your own pizza dough.

Easy Pizza Dough

¼ cup	water	50 mL
1 ½ cups	Easy Scone and Biscuit Mix (page 57)	375 mL

Combine water and Easy Biscuit Mix until dough is stiff.
Place dough on lightly floured surface and knead slightly, about 6 to 8 turns. Roll into very thin (¼ inch/5 mm) round. Place on baking sheet and pinch edge to make ridge.

Pizza

For oven-baked pizza: Spray a pizza pan with non-stick vegetable cooking oil spray or lightly grease pan. Place dough on pan. Spread with sauce, shredded cheese and add toppings as desired. Bake at 425°F (220°C) for 10 to 15 minutes or until cheese is bubbly and bottom of crust is browned.

For barbecued pizza: Grill crust over low to medium coals on the barbecue for 5 to 10 minutes until browned. Turn crust over and spread with sauce, shredded cheese, and add toppings as desired. Grill, covered, 10 to 12 minutes or until cheese is melted and pizzas are hot. If the bottom is browning too much, raise the grill or move to a cooler spot on the barbecue.

Pizza Toppings

Use toppings of your choice but *do not use* prepared meats such as pepperoni, salami or bacon, which are the primary sources of fat in a pizza. Consider these alternatives:

seafood: fish, crabmeat, mussels, clams or lobster
poultry: chicken or turkey
meat: pre-cooked ground beef or pork, drained of all fat
vegetables: tomatoes, corn kernels, onion, mushrooms, peppers (hot or sweet), eggplant (peeled), broccoli, cauliflower
cheeses: part-skim milk mozzarella, low-fat cheeses, Parmesan

Meatless Pizza

Here's an example of one of our favourite pizzas.

1	12-inch (30 cm) pizza crust	1
½ cup	tomato sauce	125 mL
1½ tsp	dried oregano	7 mL
Half	sweet green pepper, chopped	Half
1	tomato, chopped	1
½ cup	small broccoli florets	125 mL
½ cup	mushrooms, sliced	125 mL
1	small onion, sliced	1
1 cup	grated skim milk mozzarella cheese	250 mL
Pinch	hot pepper flakes (optional)	Pinch

Place crust on ungreased pizza pan or baking sheet.

Spread tomato sauce over crust and sprinkle with oregano. Top with green pepper, tomato, broccoli, mushrooms and onion; sprinkle with cheese, and hot pepper flakes (if using).

Bake at 450°F (230°C) for 10 to 15 minutes or until cheese is bubbling and crust is golden brown.

Makes 2 servings.

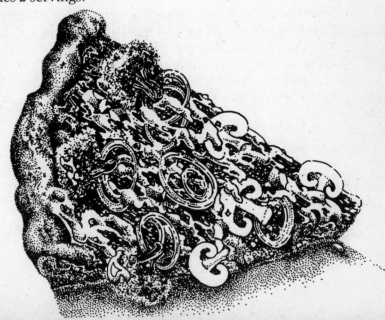

Dips and Dippers

Don't let a session of nibbling destroy your healthy eating
habits. Try these alternatives:

Fresh fruits
Low-fat cheese (skim or part-skim mozzarella, farmer's)
    and pita crisps (p. 83)
Unbuttered popcorn
Low-fat yogurt with fruit

If you can't resist dips (and dippers), we have some
suggestions for slimming down your favourite dips, as well as
some new low-fat recipes. Popular dippers like potato chips or
nacho chips are loaded with fat, calories and salt. Raw
vegetables are the very best alternative. Consider trying:

- cucumber, seeded and cut into spears
- turnip, cut into sticks
- mushrooms, cut large ones into quarters
- cherry tomatoes, with stems left on for easy dunking
- celery sticks, the tender inner stalks are best
- Belgian endive, rinse, dry and separate leaves, cutting
  off bitter core
- asparagus, snap off tough ends and use the tops
- sweet peppers, use all colours, cut in wedges
- green onions, both the white and pale green parts
- lettuce, use the small inner leaves
- zucchini, cut in strips
- carrots, whole baby carrots or sticks

Some vegetables make good dippers when they've been steamed for 3 to 5 minutes, then plunged into ice water to prevent overcooking:

- beans, green, wax or long Chinese, cut in pieces
- corn, baby ears
- cauliflower florets
- broccoli, cut into small florets

For sweeter snacks, use fibre-filled fruits such as pears, apples, oranges, nectarines and bananas to dip in 1 cup (250 mL) low-fat sour cream sweetened with brown sugar to taste.

Revising Your Dip Recipes

Make the switch from regular to lower-fat sour cream, cream cheese and mayonnaise as your first step. It can make a big difference. Be careful when substituting low-fat plain yogurt—it can make your dip runny. Instead, try half yogurt and half low-fat sour cream. Then make adjustments from there.

Instead of:			Try:		
	Calories	Grams Fat		Calories	Grams Fat
1/2 cup (125 mL) 4% cottage cheese	120	5	½ cup (125 mL) 1% cottage cheese	90	1
1 oz (30 g) cream cheese	100	10	1 oz (30 g) light cream cheese	60	5
¼ cup (50 mL) mayonnaise	400	44	¼ cup (50 mL) light mayonnaise	232	20
½ cup (125 mL) sour cream	238	23	½ cup (125 mL) low-fat sour cream	110	6.5
1 cup (250 mL) plain yogurt	139	7	1 cup (250 mL) non-fat plain yogurt	127	0

Pita Crisps

Instead of high-fat crackers, try Melba toast, whole grain or fat-free crackers or crispbreads. Make your own pita crisps or tortilla chips. It's another easy way to cut down on salt and fat.

4	6-inch (15 cm) whole wheat pitas	4

Cut through edges of pitas and separate into rounds. Cut each round into 8 wedges. Arrange smooth side down in single layers on cookie sheets.

Bake at 300°F (150°C) 10 to 12 minutes or until crisp and lightly browned. Serve warm or at room temperature. Store in airtight container.

Makes 64 crisps.

Tortilla Chips

8	8-inch (20 cm) corn tortillas	8
2 tbsp	vegetable oil	25 mL
½ tsp	coarse (kosher) salt	2 mL

Brush both sides of tortillas lightly with oil; stack oiled tortillas. Cut stack in half; cut each half into 4 wedges. Separate and arrange in single layers on cookie sheets. Sprinkle with salt.

Bake at 400°F (200°C) 6 to 8 minutes until starting to curl and crisp. Serve warm or at room temperature. Store in airtight container.

Makes 64 chips.

Spicy Pinto Bean Dip

The vegetable juice in this recipe replaces much of the fat usually found in refried beans and bean dip.

2 tsp	vegetable oil	10 mL
¼ cup	minced onion	50 mL
½ tsp	minced garlic	2 mL
½ tsp	chili powder	2 mL
Pinch	ground cumin	Pinch
1	can (16 oz/454 g) pinto beans, drained and rinsed	1
⅓ cup	vegetable juice	75 mL

In a heavy medium-sized saucepan, heat oil. Add onion and garlic; cook over medium heat 2 to 3 minutes until onion starts to soften.

Add chili powder and cumin; stir 30 seconds. Add beans and vegetable juice. Mash well with potato masher; continue cooking until slightly thickened and like a paste.

Serve warm.

Makes 1½ cups (375 mL).

Cuke and Cress Dip

In the spring, watercress grows wild in streams, or look for it in your produce section. If sour half-and-half is not available, you can make it by adding a teaspoon (5 mL) of lemon juice or vinegar to ⅓ cup (75 mL) of regular half-and-half.

2	medium cucumbers	2
1 cup	coarsely chopped watercress	250 mL
⅓ cup	soured half-and-half	75 mL
⅓ cup	plain non-fat yogurt	75 mL
2 tbsp	low-cal Italian salad dressing	25 mL

Peel cucumbers. Halve lengthwise and scrape out seeds; coarsely shred. Wrap shredded cucumber in tea towel and squeeze out excess moisture.

In a bowl, combine shredded cucumber, watercress, half-and-half, yogurt and salad dressing, mixing well.

Makes 2 cups (500 mL).

Prune Apple Butter

This high-fibre, low-fat spread is a healthy alternative to butter or margarine. Too delicious to keep to yourself, it is nice to make for friends as a gift.

1 lb	pitted prunes (2½ cups/625 mL)	500 g
3	medium tart green apples, peeled, cored and quartered	3
1½ cups	unsweetened apple juice	375 mL
⅓ cup	crystallized ginger	75 mL
1 tsp	lemon juice	5 mL

In a 12-cup (3 L) saucepan, combine prunes, apples, apple juice and ginger; bring to a boil. Reduce heat, cover and simmer gently for 10 minutes.

Uncover and continue to cook, stirring occasionally, 10 to 15 minutes or until fruits are tender and liquid is almost absorbed.

Remove from heat; stir in lemon juice. Blend in a food processor or blender until smooth. Cool.

Cover and store in refrigerator for up to 3 weeks.

Makes about 3½ cups (875 mL).

Honey Nut Spread

Especially good on raisin bread and topped with slices of kiwifruit or tomato. Enjoy, but since the nuts and seeds are high in fat, use sparingly.

2 cups	unsalted dry roasted peanuts	500 mL
¼ cup	roasted hulled sunflower seeds	50 mL
3 tbsp	vegetable oil	50 mL
1 tbsp	honey	15 mL

Process peanuts, sunflower seeds, vegetable oil and honey in a food processor or blender until mixture forms a ball. (It doesn't become really smooth.)

Cover and store in refrigerator for up to 6 weeks.

Makes 1 ½ cups (375 mL).

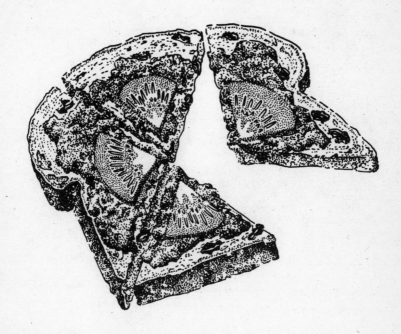

Fruit Jelly Candies

Great to make for kids' parties—no mess—and perfect for
when you feel like having something to nibble while watching
TV. Someone in our family has diabetes, so we make these
using the Jell-O with artificial sweetener—and it tastes just as
good as the conventionally sweetened variety. You can also
cut them into fingers or even fancy shapes.

3	packages (each 3 oz/100 g) Jell-O, any flavour	3
4	envelopes (¼ oz/7 g) plain gelatin	4
4 cups	boiling water	1 L

In a bowl, combine Jell-O, gelatin and boiling water; stir to
dissolve.

Pour into 9 × 13-inch (3.5 L) pan and refrigerate until firm.
Cut into 1-inch (2.5 cm) squares.

Makes 97 squares.

Fibre Kisses

Pitted prunes
Crunchy peanut butter

Flatten prunes slightly. Sandwich together in pairs with 1 tsp (5 mL) each crunchy peanut butter.

Wrap in foil or plastic wrap, twisting ends to resemble kisses.

Coffee Jellies

These candies can be stored in the refrigerator for up to a week. If serving for dessert, top with one of the low-fat dessert toppings.

1 tbsp	unflavoured gelatin	15 mL
¼ cup	cold water	50 mL
1½ cups	boiling strong coffee	375 mL
⅓ cup	granulated sugar	75 mL

In a bowl, combine gelatin and cold water.

Add coffee and sugar, stirring until dissolved. Cool.

Pour mixture into individual moulds for a dessert or pour into an 8-inch (2 L) square pan. Refrigerate until set. Cut into fingers or squares.

Makes 20 candies.

Index